WINDS

WINDS

By Mary O'Neill

Illustrated by James Barkley

DOUBLEDAY & COMPANY, INC.
GARDEN CITY, NEW YORK

Library of Congress Catalog Card Number 73–116242
Text Copyright © 1970 by Mary O'Neill
Illustrations Copyright © 1970 by James Barkley
All Rights Reserved
Printed in the United States of America
First Edition

This book is gratefully dedicated to Malford Turner.

The Canopy of Air

Between the lower levels of the air
And the blue, upper stories of the sea
The earth floor of an ever circling planet
Holds all of life we know with certainty;
While miles thick over us, mobile, transparent,
Hovers the atmospheric canopy.

Without this canopy no color, clouds or rain,
No fire, no sound, no birds aloft, no grass,
No sunlit sky, no changing greens of grain,
No fishes dimpling waters clear as glass,
No shield for meteors that fall and scar,
No tap of footsteps in approach or pass.

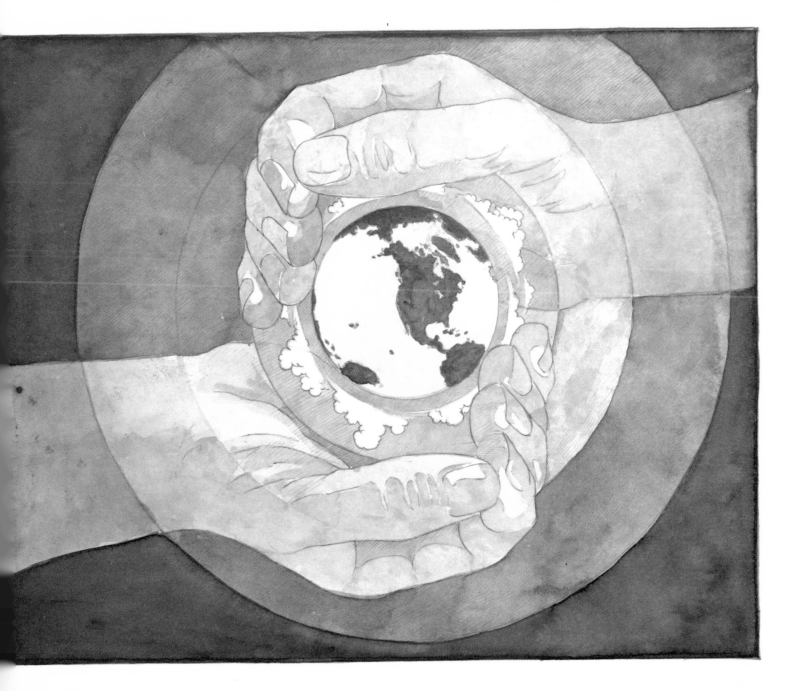

What Are You, Wind?

What are you, wind?
Only air
Winding in and out of
Everywhere?
If only air,
And thinner than all gauze,
How do you know when
To bluster and to pause?
Or where to go?
How to drift and settle
Each star-flake of snow,
To crest a wave,
Ripple stands of grain,
Make leaves talk

And slant the rain?
What are you, wind
I feel and cannot see,
You, who as breath
Are life itself to me?
How can you slap,
Slam and sting,
Break, destroy, uproot,
And yet so softly sing?
Push at apples
Until they fall,
You with no shape
And no color at all?

North Wind

Is your father
A long, sharp, glittering knife?
And did he take the bluest,
Coldest, tallest iceberg for a wife?
Did they feed you
Sharp little slivers of ice
And powdered tundra mixed
With frozen mice?
Was your mother proud
When you puffed your cheeks
And uttered your first
Howls and shrieks?
Did they teach you that any
Day was lost
Unless it carried
A chilling frost?
Did you learn that
To bite and freeze
Was better manners
Than saying: "Please"?
Did your father say:
"Go blacken leaves,

Run down collars,
Up skirts and sleeves"?
Did your mother say:
"Go nip some noses
And freeze the water
In firemen's hoses"?
Is your pencil an icicle?
Why do you cry
Sometimes in the night
Between the roof and sky?

This is your way of knowing:

A north wind or breeze
Is always three hundred and sixty degrees
From where it is blowing.
In eastern Canada it begins to course
Southward under pressures low or high
Singing softly as a lullaby
Or screaming gale-force.

South Wind

Through the sunlight
The south wind swings
In a soft dress with a flower breath,
And the sunlight smiles
Between the languid leaves.
Golden speckles shift along the grass.
Water flattens to a looking glass.
Midges float, locusts cry.
And there is only blue in the sky.

Through the sunlight
Down the rays of noon
The south wind blows
Her honeysuckle breath
Across the northern pines.
Used to the rasp of eagle wings,
Unused to soft and gentle things,
The pines, green-stiff, unmoved, let fall
Neither cone nor needle; nothing, nothing at all.

This is your way of knowing:

A south wind or breeze
Is always one hundred and eighty degrees
From where it is blowing.
It comes from the Gulf of Mexico.
The climate the south wind creates
Rolls up through our southern states
With its distinctive flow.

The East Wind

The east wind stirs the air
To a bleakness not intense, but there,
A misery of small size, a gray
That weakens rather than blots the sun away.
You can see the work of the east wind best
On high cold rocks where sea gulls rest,
For there, a busy, fog-wrapped ghost,
She carves grotesques on the Atlantic coast.

This is your way of knowing:

An east wind or breeze
Is always ninety degrees
From where it is blowing.
The east wind characteristically
Flows from frail to frantic,
From its birthplace, the Atlantic,
From its mother, the sea.

The West Wind

Sassafras, sage and tumbleweed,
Poisonous snake and cactus seed,
The move of a million buffalo,
Do you see them again when west winds blow?

And thick around you everywhere
The scream of arrows in the air,
Cowboys yelling: "Yippee-ai-oo,"
Do you hear them again when west winds blow?

And in white clouds the flying manes
Of the wild horses of the plains,
Log cabins buried in the snow,
Do you see them again when west winds blow?

The leaving home for the unknown trek
With a red bandana around your neck,
No map to tell you where to go,
Do you feel this again when west winds blow?

Or, is west wind just a wind to you
Over the fence and down the flue?
No scent of bison or buffalo
Crinkles your nose when west winds blow?

This is your way of knowing:

A west wind or breeze
Is always two hundred and seventy degrees
From where it is blowing.
Whether sunning, raining or snowing,
Strong or weak or shilly-shally
Up from the Mississippi Valley
It comes blowing.

Becalmed

The wind is still as death
On the water swell.
The boat rocks gently
Going nowhere at all.
The sails hang limp as sheets
On a country clothesline.
The day is gold and fine.

We have no trouble breathing.
Our heartbeats drum our chests.
There is enough air stirring
For the in-and-out of breath,
But not enough to push a sail over the water slap
When all the big winds lie down for a nap.

The Lee Wind

The lee wind is always putting on
No-color scarves of silk chiffon,
And when it blows it is so soft
I wonder how it stays aloft.

Jet Stream

When, like lions bursting forth,
The jet stream roars in from the north
The air grows cold and thunderclaps
Waken children from their naps;
Birds huddle and refuse to fly
And people bend as they go by.

Wind Colors the World

If wind were not always busy
Moving up, thrusting down,
To the right, to the left,
In whirls, spirals and shafts,
Stirring light like a knife, like a spoon,
To break it into all its colored rays
How dull would be the color of our days.

Pressure Systems

A pressure system is power
Pushing the wind's blow
High above the earth, or
Midway or down low;
And regulating the way
The winds will flow:
Straight, veering, fierce, fast,
Spiral or slow.
But where this pressure comes from,
Or where it will go,
How to change or control it
We do not know.

The Song Wind

The song wind is always summer.
In the sun-gold day and the opal twilight,
In the night smelling of roses and the sea,
In the dew-cleaned dawn, the song wind is always
    summer.
Little girls in loose, soft-weather dresses
With sweat-streaked hair and grime upon their
    faces,
Boys in outgrown dungarees rubbing their bare
    feet
Against each other—listen to it
In the few still moments when children are alone:
Flung on a bed, jogging on a bus,
Or not yet found in a game of hide-and-seek.
In a loneliness holy as heaven the song wind
Sings along the tender line from ear to cheek:

La, la, la la
Nails thicken on
Fingers and toes.
Time shoots you
Out of your clothes.
A thousand thoughts
Leap in your head,
And a light no sun
Has ever shed
Stirs you like a
Golden spoon
Laps up a
Sunny afternoon.
La, la, la la.
O boy, o girl

When the song wind comes
Pin it down
With both your thumbs.
For a song wind dream
Will let you see
You as you
Most long to be:
Finished, perfect,
Way up there
In a place that
Can be anywhere,
Five years from now,
Or maybe ten
As the song wind shifts
The now to then.

Talking to the Wind

Did you ever talk to the wind
When you were by yourself on a nothing-to-do-day?
When you were much younger than now
Did you ever say:
"Wind, will you tell me a story,
For you have been everywhere?"
And, did the wind seem to pay no attention
Except to wave weeds and ruffle your hair?
Then suddenly, in a dim voice
That seemed both near and far away,
You heard from inside yourself,
Or the wind, begin to say:
"Sometimes I work. Sometimes I play.
But this could be a typical day:
I circled mountaintops,
Whirled their mists away,
Flew across cities,
Put ripples in a pool,
Pushed little boys and girls
On their way to school,
Flapped clothes on clotheslines,
Knocked on window sills,

Brushed the curly coats of lambs
Upon the country hills.
I rolled noisy milk pails
Down a farmer's lane,
Tossed balls of tumbleweed
Across a Kansas plain.
I moved sulky rain clouds
To the right and left,
And widened the crack in
A granite cleft.
I swept up newspapers.
Piled hay and stacked oats,
And ran up the sleeves of
Dresses and coats.
I sailed in a bubble,
Sprayed cool from a fan,
Powered a few whistles
And rattled a pan.
I flew over an ocean,
Raced boats in a bay.
Now tell me, earthling,
What you did, today?"

To the Wind

Wind is air in motion*
Dear mechanical mixture of oxygen and carbonic
acid gas and traces of contamination in motion:

I am deeply indebted to you
For filling my lung balloons,
For without you I would be
Dead as a broiled fish
Rouged with paprika and set among parsley
On an oven-to-table dish.
I thank you for enveloping the earth,
For leaf shadows splashing on the grass,
For the ruffling of waves and the shirring of brooks,
For the drift of snowflakes and white clouds,
And the rinky-tink of rains
Bursting crystal polka dots
On windowpanes.
I like the way you carry birds,
Pushing up under their fan-spread wings
So they can coast for hours
On your broad, invisible back.
Birds, sailboats, airplanes and kites
Would have a poor life, or none, without you.
And I like the way you swing skirts and lift long hair,
The skillful and uncommon way you carve
Rocks into precipices, secret caves and crannies,

And the way you shape trees so that no two
     ever look alike.
How sweetly you bring in the spring,
Floating through the fresh wet silk of rain
All young and thin in an imagined blue
No one ever saw but everyone always knew.
I love the way you sing on summer nights,
Softly over treetops and through flowers;
And in autumn the scrapy-skitter sound
You make of falling leaves. It is so like
Sharp teeth crunching down on Cracker Jack;
And in winter dark I like to hear you wail,
For then you sound lonely and scared
And you cry for all of us.
But dear mechanical mixture of oxygen and carbonic
acid gas and traces of contamination in motion:

Why do you wait so long to clean our world?
Why do you wait until your anger at your own
     laziness
Builds up a pressure inside you that drives you into
A very frenzy of:

Blasts	Twisters
Cyclones	Waterspouts
Explosions	and
Tornadoes	Whirlwinds?

*Air is the gaseous substance which envelopes the earth
 and is breathed by all land animals. A mechanical mixture
 of oxygen, carbonic acid gas and traces of other
 substances as contamination.*The Oxford Dictionary.*

The Broom Wind

On autumn nights in the north
The broom wind comes in screaming,
Swiftly sweeping clouds across the stars,
Blinding the moon,
Banging at doors and windows, shouting:
"Winter soon. Winter soon."
Stripping branches, loosening shutters,
Knocking nests out of the crotch of trees,
Sending twigs scurrying down the street
As if they were live things clicking on long-nailed feet,
Scattering all of summer's curled and fallen leaves,
Gum wrappers and the limp petals of last flowers
Into eaves and gutters to be sogged black by rain
As straight north veers the whining weather vane.

Shut the windows, children,
Draw covers up to your chin.
When the broom wind calls
Do not let her in.
Mares in chilled meadows
Look to your foals.
Squirrels, mice and rabbits
Take to your holes.

Down in the orchard on an apple arm
Hear the ropes of the old swing creak.
The broom wind is tossing it far too high.
Hear the bones of the old tree squeak
And groan as the swing falls out of the sky.
Swaying, split from root to crest
Hear it crash and begin to die.
And never more will new birds sing,
Or buds bloom, or green fruit cling,
Or children sail on that apple swing,
Or sun or moon slip in between
Black branches feathering new green.

Tuck your blankets
Under your chin
When the broom wind blows
The winter in.
And pity the ones
Whose clothes are thin.
And pity the ones
In the broom wind's path
Who bend and bow
Before her wrath.

Sirocco

Sirocco! Hot wind from the Libyan desert
Blowing across the Mediterranean Sea,
Stinging the skin, pitting the stone
In Italy, Malta and Sicily.
Sirocco! Pelting the coast of southern France,
Dimming sun to a sulphureous light,
Darkening the moon, thickening the air and
Crying all day and all night.
Smarting the eyes and chinking the ears,
Gritting the skin and stuffing the nose,
Drifting into shoes and scalp and adding
A desert's flying weight to clothes,
Curling the roof, slitting the sail,
Shaking the house, lifting the sea,
Scattering Europe's southern edge
With Africa's debris.

Sirocco!
Born in a sand waste,
A flutter, then a baby breeze
Cooling the palm, the olive
And the almond trees.
Scented with orange and apricot,
Date, jasmine and fig,
Dream wind of the desert
Before you grew too big
And swept away the lovely things
You always soothed before—
To die in mud-sprawled madness
Upon an alien shore, Sirocco . . .

Autumn Wind

Hear the shuttles of the wind
Drawing coarse orange, brown and flaming threads
Across all of summer's bloomed-out and brittling
    flower beds.

Hear the scythes in the wind
Cutting the last of the dry wild hay
Another wind planted almost a year ago today.

Hear the sigh in the wind
For blue larkspur and lost white butterfly,
Flat, folded and finished with knowing what it means
    to die.

Waterspout

The **wild wind** dives into the sea,
Sucks into the sea with a big breath.
Now in the underblue it shapes a water tower
As surprising as death.

Wind molding water
As if it were putty or clay,
Surfacing a crystal pillar that
Spins in the sun all day.

Whirlwinds guard it;
Luminous as glass
This triumph of wind over water
That ships are afraid to pass.

Wind

What do you see when I
Sing through roses, over and under the trees,
Lift the fireflies,and pass coolly
Across your sunburned knees
On a summer night?

Boy

The roses move and the leaves stir with sound.
I see fireflies and hear petals fall.
But you, who blow across my sunburned knees,
I cannot see at all
Though I try with all my might.

I feel your fingers running through my hair.
The dust you float is settling on my feet.
The smoke you shape curls skyward, and
The smell of you is sweet.
But I can see only
The things that you do—
Why, forever and forever, wind,
Can I not see you?

Who

Who tells the wind
Where to go,
And how fast,
And how slow?
Who says: "Sing softly
Through the tall
Dry corn.
Over the bombed city
Rage and mourn.
Break snow from a cloud
And wrap the street
In a soft, immaculate
Winding sheet."
Who tells the wind?
Is it controlled by men,
Or magic? If not,
Who, then?

Who tells the wind
What to do:
Curl the smoke,
Draw the flue,
Bend the wave,
Roll the tide,
How high? How wide?
Who tells the wind
What to do?
Who told it when
The world was new,
And trees were small
In the tender sod?
Was it God?
Is it God?
For it isn't me
And it isn't you.
Who?

Wind Pictures

Look! There's a giant stretching in the sky,
A thousand white-maned horses flying by,
A house, a mother mountain with her hills,
A lazy lady posing in her frills,
Cotton floating from a thousand bales,
And a white ship with white sails.

See the old witch fumbling with her shawl,
White towers piling on a castle wall,
The bits of soft that break and fall away,
Air-borne mushrooms with undersides of gray—
Above, a white doe races with her fawn
On the white grass of a celestial lawn.
Lift up your lovely heads and look
As wind turns clouds into a picture book.

The Wind's Playmates

Clouds have names
And they live in certain places.
The wind plays with all of them and
Knows their names and their faces.

Cirrus

CIRRUS* lives highest in the sky
Cirrus is white without any shading,
Silky, detached, Cirrus moves in single drifts,
Or a feathery plume that swerves
Into tufts and immaculate curves.
Cirrus is made of ice crystals that meet
At heights above 20,000 feet.

*United States Power Squadrons Committee for
Elective Courses Weather Course, page 9.

Cumulus

CUMULUS* lives in the middle sky
At an altitude from 6,500 to 20,000 feet.
And Cumulus is formed when water droplets meet.
Cumulus is shaped in piled-up ripples or flakes
Much like frosting swirled on birthday cakes.
Cumulus is what people mean when they cry:
"Look at that beautiful 'mackerel sky'."

*United States Squadrons Committee for
Elective Courses Weather Course, page 20.

Stratus

STRATUS* lives lowest in the sky
From near ground level to 6,500 feet.
Neither very beautiful and certainly not neat
Stratus sprawls the sky like a rumpled gray sheet,
Dimming the sun and muffling sound

Stratus is called fog when it rests on the ground.
But when the wind tosses clouds together
As it often does in mixed-up weather
They combine to make wonderful forms
Rolling and banging in thunderstorms,
Posing as elephants, turrets and towns,
Lions and leopards and puffballs and clowns.

*United States Power Squadrons Committee for
Elective Courses Weather Course, page 38.

Weather

WEATHER: the condition of the atmosphere
(at a given place and time) with respect
to heat, cold, presence or absence of rain, etc.*

*The Oxford Dictionary.

Atmosphere

ATMOSPHERE: The whole body of terrestrial
air. A pressure of 14.7 pounds on the square inch,
which is that of the atmosphere on the
earth's surface 1830.*

Weather is the condition of the atmosphere:
Warm, dry, soggy, hot, cold, clear.
And atmosphere is the body of terrestrial air
The wind is always moving everywhere.
We live within this atmospheric state,
Surrounded by its ever-pushing weight.
Small wonder we grow tired and sometimes fuss
With 14.7 pounds of pressure on every square inch
    of us.

Water is always present in the atmosphere.
You can feel *solid* water when winds blow
In ice, sleet, frost, crystalline clouds or snow.
As a *liquid* air water is most familiar to you
In rain, mist, fog or diamond dots of dew.
But in the air's eternally shifting scheme
Water is often a *gas* as in vapor or dry steam.
In every season, in weather foul or fair,
Water is always present in the air.

*The Oxford Dictionary.

Wind from an Airplane Window

Were you ever up higher than birds can fly?
So high clouds down *below*
Were great, fat, wallowing swirls
Of sky-swimming snow?
And, while you watched
Did the airplane seem to grow smaller
As the cloud mass grew higher
And thicker and taller,
And the blue at the window
Changed to milky white,
Blotting all of the known world out of sight?
And then the wind came.
And the clouds began to run,
Flattened, like sheep backs
Gilded with sun,
And in the sky the clear, incomparable blue
Stretched like a circus tent again above the
      plane and you?

Fog

Fog is a cloud
Resting on the surface of the earth.
The wind blows it away.

**United States Power Squadrons Committee for
Elective Courses Weather Course*, page 50.

MARY O'NEILL was raised in Berea, Ohio, where she wrote and directed plays for her younger brothers and sisters. She was educated at Our Lady of Lourdes Academy, Saint Joseph's Academy and Western Reserve in Cleveland and the University of Michigan. She is the mother of three children and the grandmother of three.

JAMES BARKLEY was born in New York City. Since his graduation from The School of Visual Arts eight years ago he has illustrated seven books and has had five one-man shows. He lives with his wife and child in Yonkers, New York.